THE ROYAL HORTICULTURAL SOCIETY

DIARY 2011

Commentary by
Brent Elliott

Illustrations from
the Royal Horticultural Society's
Lindley Library

F

FRANCES LINCOLN LIMITED
PUBLISHERS

Frances Lincoln Limited
4 Torriano Mews
Torriano Avenue
London NW5 2RZ
www.franceslincoln.com

The Royal Horticultural Society Diary 2011
Copyright © Frances Lincoln limited 2010

Text and illustrations copyright © the Royal
Horticultural Society 2010
and printed under licence granted by the Royal
Horticultural Society, Registered Charity number
222879/SCO38262. For more information visit our
website or call 0845 130 4646
An interest in gardening is all you need to enjoy being
a member of the RHS.
Website: www.rhs.org.uk

First Frances Lincoln edition 2010

Astronomical information © Crown Copyright.
Reproduced by permission of the Controller of Her
Majesty's Stationery Office and the UK Hydrographic
Office (www.ukho.gov.uk)
Every effort is made to ensure calendarial data is
correct at the time of going to press but the publisher
cannot accept any liability for any errors or changes.

A catalogue record for this book is available from the
British Library

ISBN: 978-0-7112-3163-4

Printed in China

1 2 3 4 5 6 7 8 9

RHS FLOWER SHOWS 2011

Regrettably Flower Show dates are no longer included in this
diary. Show date changes after publication caused confusion.
The following dates were correct at the time of going to press
but, due to circumstances beyond our control, show dates
often change in the interim period so **please confirm before
travelling**. Neither the RHS or the publisher can accept liability
for any errors.

Cardiff Flower Show (April 8–10, 2011), The Chelsea Flower
Show (May 24–28, 2011), Hampton Court Palace Flower Show
(July 5–10, 2011) and Tatton Park Flower Show (July 20–24,
2011), Malvern Flower Shows (May 12–15 and Sept 24–25, 2011)
and themed London Shows throughout the year.

RHS Flower Show Information
Can be found by visiting www.rhs.org.uk or telephoning the
24-hour Flower Show Information Line (020 7649 1885)

PICTURE CAPTIONS

Front cover *Nerine* 'Mansellii', *Nerine flexuosa* 'Alba' × *Nerine*
'Lady St Oswald'. Coloured drawing by Lilian Snelling, made
for H.J. Elwes of Colesbourne in December 1916.

Back cover *Allium wallichii*. Coloured drawing, undated, by
Lilian Snelling.

Title page *Menziesia ciliicalyx*. Coloured drawing, undated,
by Lilian Snelling, probably made for H.J. Elwes.

Overleaf, left *Paeonia whittmanniana* [sic = *wittmanniana*] var.
nudicarpa. Coloured drawing by Lilian Snelling, made in
May 1931.

CALENDAR 2011

JANUARY

M	T	W	T	F	S	S
					1	2
3	4	5	6	7	8	9
10	11	12	13	14	15	16
17	18	19	20	21	22	23
24	25	26	27	28	29	30
31						

FEBRUARY

M	T	W	T	F	S	S
1	2	3	4	5	6	
7	8	9	10	11	12	13
14	15	16	17	18	19	20
21	22	23	24	25	26	27
28						

MARCH

M	T	W	T	F	S	S
1	2	3	4	5	6	
7	8	9	10	11	12	13
14	15	16	17	18	19	20
21	22	23	24	25	26	27
28	29	30	31			

APRIL

M	T	W	T	F	S	S
				1	2	3
4	5	6	7	8	9	10
11	12	13	14	15	16	17
18	19	20	21	22	23	24
25	26	27	28	29	30	

MAY

M	T	W	T	F	S	S
						1
2	3	4	5	6	7	8
9	10	11	12	13	14	15
16	17	18	19	20	21	22
23	24	25	26	27	28	29
30	31					

JUNE

M	T	W	T	F	S	S
	1	2	3	4	5	
6	7	8	9	10	11	12
13	14	15	16	17	18	19
20	21	22	23	24	25	26
27	28	29	30			

JULY

M	T	W	T	F	S	S
				1	2	3
4	5	6	7	8	9	10
11	12	13	14	15	16	17
18	19	20	21	22	23	24
25	26	27	28	29	30	31

AUGUST

M	T	W	T	F	S	S
1	2	3	4	5	6	7
8	9	10	11	12	13	14
15	16	17	18	19	20	21
22	23	24	25	26	27	28
29	30	31				

SEPTEMBER

M	T	W	T	F	S	S
			1	2	3	4
5	6	7	8	9	10	11
12	13	14	15	16	17	18
19	20	21	22	23	24	25
26	27	28	29	30		

OCTOBER

M	T	W	T	F	S	S
					1	2
3	4	5	6	7	8	9
10	11	12	13	14	15	16
17	18	19	20	21	22	23
24	25	26	27	28	29	30
31						

NOVEMBER

M	T	W	T	F	S	S
1	2	3	4	5	6	
7	8	9	10	11	12	13
14	15	16	17	18	19	20
21	22	23	24	25	26	27
28	29	30				

DECEMBER

M	T	W	T	F	S	S
			1	2	3	4
5	6	7	8	9	10	11
12	13	14	15	16	17	18
19	20	21	22	23	24	25
26	27	28	29	30	31	

CALENDAR 2012

JANUARY

M	T	W	T	F	S	S
						1
2	3	4	5	6	7	8
9	10	11	12	13	14	15
16	17	18	19	20	21	22
23	24	25	26	27	28	29
30	31					

FEBRUARY

M	T	W	T	F	S	S
	1	2	3	4	5	
6	7	8	9	10	11	12
13	14	15	16	17	18	19
20	21	22	23	24	25	26
27	28	29				

MARCH

M	T	W	T	F	S	S
			1	2	3	4
5	6	7	8	9	10	11
12	13	14	15	16	17	18
19	20	21	22	23	24	25
26	27	28	29	30	31	

APRIL

M	T	W	T	F	S	S
						1
2	3	4	5	6	7	8
9	10	11	12	13	14	15
16	17	18	19	20	21	22
23	24	25	26	27	28	29
30						

MAY

M	T	W	T	F	S	S
	1	2	3	4	5	6
7	8	9	10	11	12	13
14	15	16	17	18	19	20
21	22	23	24	25	26	27
28	29	30	31			

JUNE

M	T	W	T	F	S	S
				1	2	3
4	5	6	7	8	9	10
11	12	13	14	15	16	17
18	19	20	21	22	23	24
25	26	27	28	29	30	

JULY

M	T	W	T	F	S	S
						1
2	3	4	5	6	7	8
9	10	11	12	13	14	15
16	17	18	19	20	21	22
23	24	25	26	27	28	29
30	31					

AUGUST

M	T	W	T	F	S	S
	1	2	3	4	5	
6	7	8	9	10	11	12
13	14	15	16	17	18	19
20	21	22	23	24	25	26
27	28	29	30	31		

SEPTEMBER

M	T	W	T	F	S	S
					1	2
3	4	5	6	7	8	9
10	11	12	13	14	15	16
17	18	19	20	21	22	23
24	25	26	27	28	29	30

OCTOBER

M	T	W	T	F	S	S
1	2	3	4	5	6	7
8	9	10	11	12	13	14
15	16	17	18	19	20	21
22	23	24	25	26	27	28
29	30	31				

NOVEMBER

M	T	W	T	F	S	S
			1	2	3	4
5	6	7	8	9	10	11
12	13	14	15	16	17	18
19	20	21	22	23	24	25
26	27	28	29	30		

DECEMBER

M	T	W	T	F	S	S
					1	2
3	4	5	6	7	8	9
10	11	12	13	14	15	16
17	18	19	20	21	22	23
24	25	26	27	28	29	30
31						

Lilian Snelling

Paeonia Whittmanniana
May 15. 1931 *var nudicarpa*

LILIAN SNELLING 1879–1972

"Her work as a botanical artist is without living peer [and] as a botanical illustrator and technician her work materially eclipses that of Redoute," wrote the distinguished botanist Dr George Lawrence, on hearing of the death of Lilian Snelling.

Lilian Snelling was born in St Mary Cray in Kent to a well-known family of millers. The youngest of the family, she spent most of her life in St Mary Cray, living with her three other unmarried sisters in Spring Hall, the family home. The illustrations in this volume represent examples of her work throughout her career. The examples of her earliest surviving work were painted in the fields and hedgerows of Kent around St Mary Cray and nearby Tunbridge Wells. These composite pictures, which formed the sketchbook she kept in her early twenties, were completed over a period of time.

After studying art and lithography at the Royal College of Art in London, she worked as the protégée of the arboriculturalist and plant hunter Henry John Elwes (1846–1922), painting plants that grew in his garden at Colesbourne in Gloucestershire. Many of these images are included in this diary. (When Arthur Grove published two supplements to Elwes' *Monograph of the Genus Lilium*, 1933–40, it was to Lilian Snelling that he turned for the magnificent illustrations, which are regarded as her masterpiece.)

From 1916 to 1921 Lilian Snelling worked at the Royal Botanic Garden, Edinburgh, under the guidance of the Keeper, Sir Isaac Bayley Balfour, and it was there that she developed the meticulous style that was to stand her in such good stead on *Curtis's Botanical Magazine*, which had been purchased by the Royal Horticultural Society in 1921.

In 1922 she was hired as the magazine's principal illustrator and lithographer and, over a period of thirty years, she made over 740 plates, an achievement that put her at the forefront of her art. Volume 169 was dedicated to her, with praise for her "remarkable delicacy of accurate outlines, brilliancy of colour and intricate gradation of tone".

Lilian Snelling retired from the *Botanical Magazine* in 1952. She was awarded the MBE in 1954 and the Victoria Medal of Honour, the Royal Horticultural Society's highest award, in 1955. The last of the sisters to survive, she died at the age of ninety-three.

The flowering of Lilian Snelling's mature style formed the outstanding model for British botanical artists since then. The illustrations in this diary represent examples from all periods of her long career.

Brent Elliott

THE ROYAL HORTICULTURAL SOCIETY

DECEMBER & JANUARY

27 *Monday*   Holiday, UK, Republic of Ireland, Australia and New Zealand

28 *Tuesday*   Holiday, UK and New Zealand
Last Quarter

29 *Wednesday*

30 *Thursday*

31 *Friday*   New Year's Eve
Holiday, USA

1 *Saturday*   New Year's Day

2 *Sunday*

Dendrobium Thwaitesiae. Coloured drawing, dated April 1915,
by Lilian Snelling, probably made for H.J. Elwes.

Holiday, UK, Republic of Ireland, Canada,
Australia and New Zealand

Monday **3**

Holiday, Scotland and New Zealand
New Moon

Tuesday **4**

Wednesday **5**

Epiphany

Thursday **6**

Friday **7**

Saturday **8**

Sunday **9**

Iris xiphium 'Pur-sind' (a hybrid bred by the Dutch nursery house
of Van Tubergen, a cross between *Iris persica* 'Purpurea' and *Iris
sindjarensis* [now *Iris aucheri*]). Coloured drawing by Lilian Snelling,
made for H.J. Elwes of Colesbourne in March 1915.

JANUARY

10 *Monday*

11 *Tuesday*

12 *Wednesday*   *First Quarter*

13 *Thursday*

14 *Friday*

15 *Saturday*

16 *Sunday*

Coelogyne corymbosa. Coloured drawing by Lilian Snelling,
made in March 1915 for H.J. Elwes of Colesbourne,
who had collected the plant in Sikkim the previous year.

JANUARY

Holiday, USA (Martin Luther King's Birthday)

Monday **17**

Tuesday **18**

Full Moon

Wednesday **19**

Thursday **20**

Friday **21**

Saturday **22**

Sunday **23**

Crocus imperati and *Crocus sieberi* subsp. *atticus*.
Coloured drawing by Lilian Snelling, made for
H.J. Elwes of Colesbourne in February 1915.

JANUARY & FEBRUARY

Monday **31**

Tuesday **1**

Wednesday **2**

Chinese New Year
New Moon

Thursday **3**

Friday **4**

Saturday **5**

Accession of Queen Elizabeth II
Holiday, New Zealand (Waitangi Day)

Sunday **6**

Leucojum vernum var. *carpathicum* 'Multiflora'.
Coloured drawing by Lilian Snelling, made for
H.J. Elwes of Colesbourne in February 1916.

FEBRUARY

7 *Monday*

8 *Tuesday*

9 *Wednesday*

10 *Thursday*

11 *Friday*   *First Quarter*

12 *Saturday*

13 *Sunday*

*Primula vulgaris, Hyacinthoides non-scripta, Primula
veris, Parietaria judaica*: an early coloured drawing by
Lilian Snelling of plants around her family home at
St Mary Cray, made from May to August 1901.

II.
Wild Hyacinth. Bluebell.
Scilla Festalis.

Wood. Burwash.

May 6. 1901.

I.

II.

I.
Primrose.
Primula Acaulis.
Woods. Burwash.

May 6. 1901.

III. Cowslip. Paigle.
Primula veris.
Tunbridge Wells.

May 5. 1901.

I

V

Common Pellitory -of -the -wall.
Parietaria officinalis.
Cockmanning's. August 23. 1901.

FEBRUARY

St. Valentine's Day

Monday **14**

Tuesday **15**

Wednesday **16**

Thursday **17**

Full Moon

Friday **18**

Saturday **19**

Sunday **20**

Cymbidium Alexanderi. Coloured drawing by Lilian Snelling,
made for H.J. Elwes of Colesbourne in 1915.

FEBRUARY

21 *Monday*   Holiday, USA (Washington's Birthday)

22 *Tuesday*

23 *Wednesday*

24 *Thursday*   *Last Quarter*

25 *Friday*

26 *Saturday*

27 *Sunday*

Narcissus pseudonarcissus. Coloured drawing,
undated, by Lilian Snelling.

4.

Amaryllideæ.
narcissus.
1. Pseudo-narcissus.
Common Daffodil, Lent Lily.

"Southover". Burwash
Sussex.

L.S.

FEBRUARY & MARCH

Monday **28**

St. David's Day

Tuesday **1**

Wednesday **2**

Thursday **3**

New Moon

Friday **4**

Saturday **5**

Sunday **6**

Rhododendron dauricum 'Sempervirens'. Hand-coloured
proof plate by Lilian Snelling, for plate 8930 of *Curtis's
Botanical Magazine* (1938).

7 *Monday*

---

8 *Tuesday*   Shrove Tuesday

---

9 *Wednesday*   Ash Wednesday

---

10 *Thursday*

---

11 *Friday*

---

12 *Saturday*   *First Quarter*

---

13 *Sunday*

Primula × anisodoxa. Coloured drawing, dated May 1916,
by Lilian Snelling, made at the Edinburgh Botanic Garden.

MARCH

Commonwealth Day

Monday **14**

Tuesday **15**

Wednesday **16**

St. Patrick's Day
Holiday, Northern Ireland and Republic of Ireland

Thursday **17**

Friday **18**

Full Moon

Saturday **19**

Vernal Equinox (Spring begins)

Sunday **20**

Prunus avium. Coloured drawing, undated, by Lilian Snelling.

MARCH

21 *Monday*

22 *Tuesday*

23 *Wednesday*

24 *Thursday*

25 *Friday*

26 *Saturday*   *Last Quarter*

27 *Sunday*   British Summer Time begins

Tulipa fosteriana. Coloured drawing by Lilian Snelling,
made for H.J. Elwes of Colesbourne in April 1905.

MARCH & APRIL

Monday **28**

Tuesday **29**

Wednesday **30**

Thursday **31**

Friday **1**

Saturday **2**

Mother's Day, UK
New Moon

Sunday **3**

Omphalodes luciliae. Coloured drawing by Lilian Snelling,
made for H.J. Elwes of Colesbourne in September 1915.

APRIL

4 *Monday*

5 *Tuesday*

6 *Wednesday*

7 *Thursday*

8 *Friday*

9 *Saturday*

10 *Sunday*

Five species of *Erythronium: E. hendersonii, E. johnstoni* [sic = *johnsoni*],
E. revolutum, E. hartwegi, and *E. americanum*. Coloured drawing by
Lilian Snelling, made for H.J. Elwes of Colesbourne in April 1915.

APRIL

First Quarter

Monday **11**

Tuesday **12**

Wednesday **13**

Thursday **14**

Friday **15**

Saturday **16**

Palm Sunday

Sunday **17**

Iris 'Mrs Barnard'. Coloured drawing, dated January 1952,
by Lilian Snelling, made from a specimen provided
by Mrs Stevenson of Balesmead.

APRIL

18 *Monday*   *Full Moon*

19 *Tuesday*   First Day of Passover (Pesach)

20 *Wednesday*

21 *Thursday*   Birthday of Queen Elizabeth II
Maundy Thursday

22 *Friday*   Good Friday
Holiday, UK, Canada, Australia and New Zealand

23 *Saturday*   St. George's Day
Holiday, Australia

24 *Sunday*   Easter Sunday

Fritillaria latifolia. Coloured drawing by Lilian Snelling,
made for H.J. Elwes of Colesbourne in April 1915.

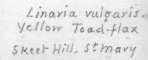

Linaria vulgaris.
Yellow Toad-flax
Skeet Hill, St Mary

.Snelling.

APRIL & MAY

Easter Monday Holiday,
UK (exc. Scotland), Republic of Ireland,
Australia and New Zealand
Anzac Day (Australia and New Zealand)
Last Quarter

Monday **25**

Holiday, Australia (Anzac Day) (subject to confirmation)

Tuesday **26**

Wednesday **27**

Thursday **28**

Friday **29**

Saturday **30**

Sunday **1**

Linaria vulgaris. Coloured drawing, undated, by Lilian Snelling.

2 *Monday*   Early Spring Bank Holiday, UK and Republic of Ireland

3 *Tuesday*   *New Moon*

4 *Wednesday*

5 *Thursday*

6 *Friday*

7 *Saturday*

8 *Sunday*   Mother's Day, USA, Canada, Australia and New Zealand

Paeonia clusii. Coloured drawing by Lilian Snelling, for a plate in Sir
Frederick Stern's *Study of the genus Paeonia* (1946).

MAY

Monday **9**

First Quarter

Tuesday **10**

Wednesday **11**

Thursday **12**

Friday **13**

Saturday **14**

Sunday **15**

Anemone blanda var. *scythinica*, 3 April 1916. Coloured drawing by
Lilian Snelling, made for H.J. Elwes of Colesbourne in April 1916.

MAY

WEEK **21**

16 *Monday*

17 *Tuesday*   *Full Moon*

18 *Wednesday*

19 *Thursday*

20 *Friday*

21 *Saturday*

22 *Sunday*

Paeonia anomala var. *intermedia*. Coloured drawing,
dated May 1931, by Lilian Snelling, for a plate in
Sir Frederick Stern's *Study of the genus Paeonia* (1946).

Paeonia anomala var intermedia
May 15th 1931

an Snelling

MAY

Holiday, Canada (Victoria Day)

Monday **23**

Last Quarter

Tuesday **24**

Wednesday **25**

Thursday **26**

Friday **27**

Saturday **28**

Sunday **29**

Primula capitata. Coloured drawing by Lilian Snelling,
made for H.J. Elwes of Colesbourne in November 1915.

MAY & JUNE

---

30 *Monday*   Spring Bank Holiday, UK
                                              Holiday, USA (Memorial Day)

---

31 *Tuesday*

---

1 *Wednesday*   *New Moon*

---

2 *Thursday*   Ascension Day
                                                          Coronation Day

---

3 *Friday*

---

4 *Saturday*

---

5 *Sunday*

Bellis rotundifolia var. *caerulescens*. Coloured drawing,
undated but made in the 1930s, by Lilian Snelling.

JUNE

Holiday, Republic of Ireland
Holiday, New Zealand (The Queen's Birthday)

Monday **6**

Tuesday **7**

Feast of Weeks (Shavuot)

Wednesday **8**

First Quarter

Thursday **9**

Friday **10**

The Queen's Official Birthday (subject to confirmation)

Saturday **11**

Whit Sunday (Pentecost)

Sunday **12**

Papaver rhoeas. Coloured drawing, undated, by Lilian Snelling.

JUNE

---

13 *Monday*   Holiday, Australia (The Queen's Birthday)

---

14 *Tuesday*

---

15 *Wednesday*   *Full Moon*

---

16 *Thursday*

---

17 *Friday*

---

18 *Saturday*

---

19 *Sunday*   Father's Day, UK, Canada and USA
Trinity Sunday

Allium wallichii. Coloured drawing, undated, by Lilian Snelling.

JUNE

Monday **20**

Summer Solstice (Summer begins)

Tuesday **21**

Wednesday **22**

Corpus Christi
Last Quarter

Thursday **23**

Friday **24**

Saturday **25**

Sunday **26**

Orchis pyramidalis [now *Anacamptis pyramidalis*].
Coloured drawing, undated, by Lilian Snelling,
made from a specimen in Downe, Kent.

JUNE & JULY

27 *Monday*

28 *Tuesday*

29 *Wednesday*

30 *Thursday*

1 *Friday*

Holiday, Canada (Canada Day)
New Moon

2 *Saturday*

3 *Sunday*

Edraianthus serpyllifolium [sic = *serpyllifolius*; now *Campanula serpyllifolia*]. Coloured drawing, dated 1932, by Lilian Snelling, made from a specimen provided by Sir Frederick Stern.

JULY

Holiday, USA (Independence Day)

Monday **4**

Tuesday **5**

Wednesday **6**

Thursday **7**

First Quarter

Friday **8**

Saturday **9**

Sunday **10**

Meconopsis grandis. Coloured drawing by Lilian Snelling, made while working at the Edinburgh Botanic Garden in June 1916.

JULY

11 *Monday*

12 *Tuesday*

Holiday, Northern Ireland (Battle of the Boyne)

13 *Wednesday*

14 *Thursday*

15 *Friday*

St. Swithin's Day
Full Moon

16 *Saturday*

17 *Sunday*

Carduus sp. Coloured drawing by Lilian Snelling,
made from a specimen found at Corstorphine,
while working at the Edinburgh Botanic Garden in 1918.

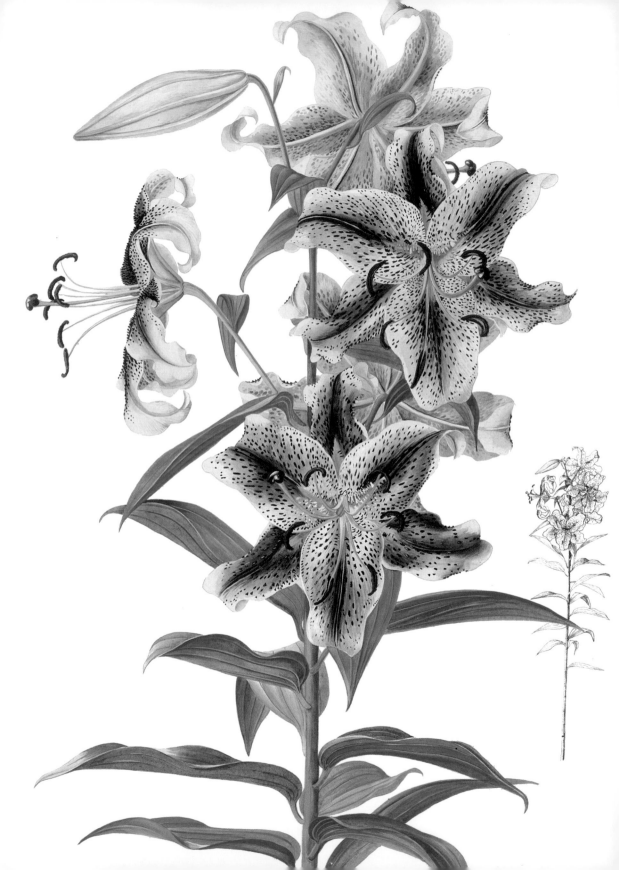

JULY

Monday **18**

Tuesday **19**

Wednesday **20**

Thursday **21**

Friday **22**

Last Quarter

Saturday **23**

Sunday **24**

Lilium × parkmanni. Coloured drawing, undated, by Lilian Snelling.

JULY

25 *Monday*

26 *Tuesday*

27 *Wednesday*

28 *Thursday*

29 *Friday*

30 *Saturday*   *New Moon*

31 *Sunday*

Verbascum nigrum. Coloured drawing, undated, by Lilian Snelling.

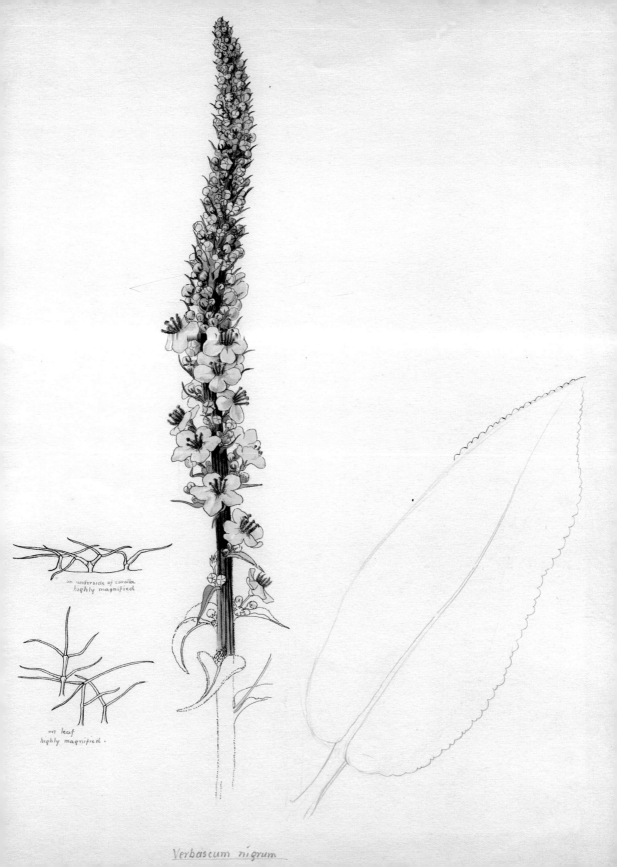

on underside of corolla
highly magnified

on leaf
highly magnified.

Verbascum nigrum

AUGUST

Summer Bank Holiday, Scotland
Holiday, Republic of Ireland
First Day of Ramadân (subject to sighting of the moon)

Monday **1**

Tuesday **2**

Wednesday **3**

Thursday **4**

Friday **5**

First Quarter

Saturday **6**

Sunday **7**

Convolvulus arvensis. Coloured drawing, undated, by Lilian
Snelling, made from a specimen found on the Isle of Wight.

AUGUST

8 *Monday*

9 *Tuesday*

10 *Wednesday*

11 *Thursday*

12 *Friday*

13 *Saturday*   *Full Moon*

14 *Sunday*

Kniphofia galpinii. Original drawing by Lilian Snelling,
for plate 8928 of *Curtis's Botanical Magazine* (1938).

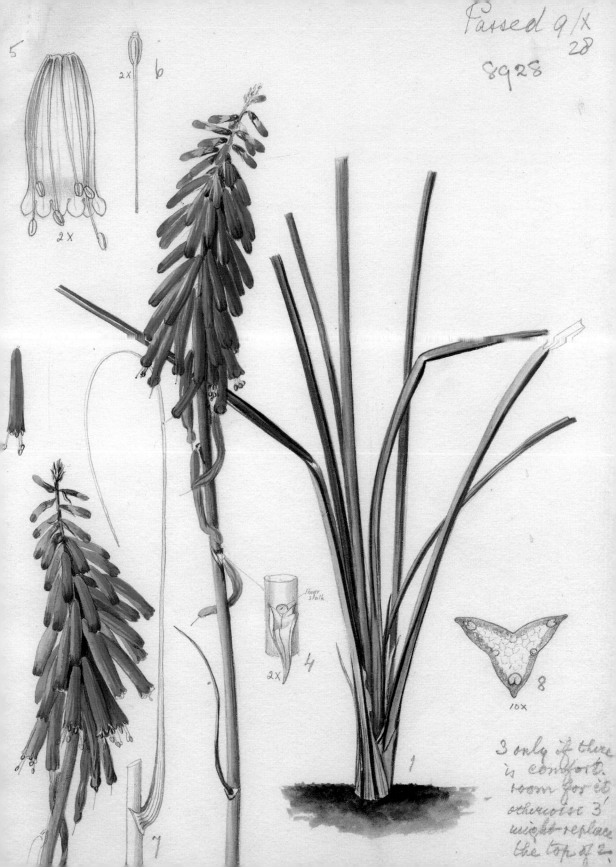

5

2X 6

2X

2X

flower stalk

4

2X

8

10X

1

7

3 only if there is comfort. room for it otherwise 3' might replace the top of 2

Bud from below
2

3

3×

2×
4

5

4×

3× 6

Paulownia Fargesii
May 30 · 1929

Lilian Snelling

1.

AUGUST

Monday **15**

Tuesday **16**

Wednesday **17**

Thursday **18**

Friday **19**

Saturday **20**

Last Quarter

Sunday **21**

Paulownia tomentosa 'Lilacina'. Original drawing by Lilian
Snelling, described by her as *Paulownia fargesii*,
for plate 8926–7 of *Curtis's Botanical Magazine* (1938),
where it bore the name *Paulownia lilacina*.

AUGUST

22 *Monday*

23 *Tuesday*

24 *Wednesday*

25 *Thursday*

26 *Friday*

27 *Saturday*

28 *Sunday*

Lathyrus sylvestris. Coloured drawing,
undated, by Lilian Snelling.

AUGUST & SEPTEMBER

Summer Bank Holiday, UK (exc. Scotland)
New Moon

Monday **29**

Tuesday **30**

Wednesday **31**

Thursday **1**

Friday **2**

Saturday **3**

Father's Day, Australia and New Zealand
First Quarter

Sunday **4**

Vallota × gastronema. Coloured drawing, dated September 1915,
by Lilian Snelling, of a hybrid raised at Colesbourne by H.J. Elwes.

SEPTEMBER

5 *Monday*

6 *Tuesday*

7 *Wednesday*

8 *Thursday*

9 *Friday*

10 *Saturday*

11 *Sunday*

Anemonopsis macrophylla. Coloured drawing by Lilian Snelling, made for H.J. Elwes of Colesbourne in August 1915.

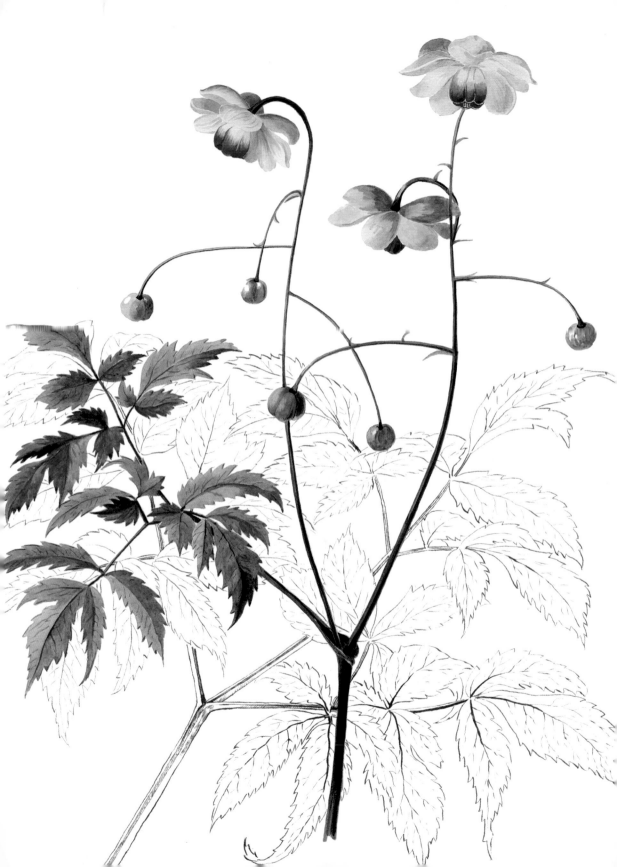

SEPTEMBER

Full Moon

Monday **12**

Tuesday **13**

Wednesday **14**

Thursday **15**

Friday **16**

Saturday **17**

Sunday **18**

Littonia modesta. Coloured drawing by Lilian Snelling,
made for H.J. Elwes of Colesbourne in August 1916.

SEPTEMBER

WEEK **39**

---

19 *Monday*

---

20 *Tuesday* *Last Quarter*

---

21 *Wednesday*

---

22 *Thursday*

---

23 *Friday* Autumnal Equinox (Autumn begins)

---

24 *Saturday*

---

25 *Sunday*

Nerine 'Mansellii', *Nerine flexuosa* 'Alba' × *Nerine* 'Lady St Oswald'.
coloured drawing by Lilian Snelling, made for H.J. Elwes of
Colesbourne in December 1916.

SEPTEMBER & OCTOBER

Monday **26**

New Moon

Tuesday **27**

Wednesday **28**

Michaelmas Day
Jewish New Year (Rosh Hashanah)

Thursday **29**

Friday **30**

Saturday **1**

Sunday **2**

Pyrus aria [now *Sorbus aria*]. Coloured drawing,
undated, by Lilian Snelling.

OCTOBER

3 *Monday*

4 *Tuesday*   *First Quarter*

5 *Wednesday*

6 *Thursday*

7 *Friday*

8 *Saturday*   Day of Atonement (Yom Kippur)

9 *Sunday*

Urceolina aurea [now *Urceolina pendula*]. Coloured drawing
by Lilian Snelling, made for H.J. Elwes of Colesbourne
in September 1914.

OCTOBER

Holiday, USA (Columbus Day)
Holiday, Canada (Thanksgiving)

Monday **10**

Tuesday **11**

Full Moon

Wednesday **12**

First Day of Tabernacles (Succoth)

Thursday **13**

Friday **14**

Saturday **15**

Sunday **16**

Amaryllis belladonna 'Hathor'. Coloured drawing, undated,
by Lilian Snelling, for a plate published in the *Journal of the
Royal Horticultural Society* in 1951, to accompany an article by
Hugh Farmar about *Amaryllis belladonna* and its cultivars.

OCTOBER

17 *Monday*

18 *Tuesday*

19 *Wednesday*

20 *Thursday*   *Last Quarter*

21 *Friday*

22 *Saturday*

23 *Sunday*

Top: *Rubus fruticosus*. Coloured drawing, undated.
Bottom: *Viburnum opulus*. Coloured drawing, undated.
Both by Lilian Snelling.

OCTOBER

Holiday, New Zealand (Labour Day)
United Nations Day

Monday **24**

Tuesday **25**

New Moon

Wednesday **26**

Thursday **27**

Friday **28**

Saturday **29**

British Summer Time ends

Sunday **30**

Oxalis lobata [now *Oxalis perdicaria*]. Coloured drawing by Lilian
Snelling, made for H.J. Elwes of Colesbourne in September 1915.

OCTOBER & NOVEMBER

31 *Monday*

Hallowe'en
Holiday, Republic of Ireland

1 *Tuesday*

All Saints' Day

2 *Wednesday*

First Quarter

3 *Thursday*

4 *Friday*

5 *Saturday*

Guy Fawkes' Day

6 *Sunday*

Dipsacus pilosus. Coloured drawing, dated August 1933,
by Lilian Snelling, based on a specimen found in Somerset.

NOVEMBER

Monday **7**

Tuesday **8**

Wednesday **9**

Full Moon

Thursday **10**

Holiday, USA (Veterans Day)
Holiday, Canada (Remembrance Day)

Friday **11**

Saturday **12**

Remembrance Sunday, UK

Sunday **13**

Choananthus cyrtanthiflorus [now *Haemanthus cyrtanthiflorus*]. Coloured
drawing by Lilian Snelling, made for H.J. Elwes of Colesbourne in August
15. It bears a label stating that W.B. Turrill, the future Keeper of the Kew
barium but then still a young assistant, determined the name.

NOVEMBER

14 *Monday*

15 *Tuesday*

16 *Wednesday*

17 *Thursday*

18 *Friday*   *Last Quarter*

19 *Saturday*

20 *Sunday*

Schisandra sphenanthera. Hand-coloured proof plate by Lilian
Snelling, for plate 8921 of *Curtis's Botanical Magazine* (1938)

8921.

L. Snelling del. et lith.

NOVEMBER

Monday **21**

Tuesday **22**

Wednesday **23**

Holiday, USA (Thanksgiving Day)

Thursday **24**

New Moon

Friday **25**

Saturday **26**

First Sunday in Advent
Islamic New Year (subject to sighting of the moon)

Sunday **27**

Bessera elegans. Coloured drawing by Lilian Snelling,
made for H.J. Elwes of Colesbourne in October 1915.

NOVEMBER & DECEMBER

28 *Monday*

29 *Tuesday*

30 *Wednesday*   St. Andrew's Day

1 *Thursday*

2 *Friday*   *First Quarter*

3 *Saturday*

4 *Sunday*

Bromelia sp. Coloured drawing, undated, by Lilian Snelling.

DECEMBER

Monday **5**

Tuesday **6**

Wednesday **7**

Thursday **8**

Friday **9**

Full Moon

Saturday **10**

Sunday **11**

Cymbidium sp. Coloured drawing, undated, by Lilian Snelling.

DECEMBER

12 *Monday*

13 *Tuesday*

14 *Wednesday*

15 *Thursday*

16 *Friday*

17 *Saturday*

18 *Sunday*   *Last Quarter*

Calceolaria 'John Innes'. Coloured drawing by Lilian Snelling,
made for H.J. Elwes of Colesbourne in July 1916.

Monday **19**

Tuesday **20**

Wednesday **21**

Winter Solstice (Winter begins)

Thursday **22**

Friday **23**

Christmas Eve
New Moon

Saturday **24**

Christmas Day

Sunday **25**

Rhododendron vernicosum. Hand-coloured proof plate by Lilian
Snelling, for plate 8904–5 of *Curtis's Botanical Magazine* (1938).

DECEMBER & JANUARY

26 *Monday*

Boxing Day (St. Stephen's Day)
Holiday, UK, Republic of Ireland, USA, Canada,
Australia and New Zealand

27 *Tuesday*

Holiday, UK, Australia and New Zealand

28 *Wednesday*

29 *Thursday*

30 *Friday*

31 *Saturday*

New Year's Eve

1 *Sunday*

New Year's Day

Erica vagans. Coloured drawing, dated August 1936, by Lilian
Snelling, based on a specimen found at Coverack in Cornwall.

JANUARY 2012

2 *Monday*   Holiday, UK, USA, Australia and New Zealand

3 *Tuesday*   Holiday, Scotland and New Zealand

4 *Wednesday*

5 *Thursday*

6 *Friday*

7 *Saturday*

8 *Sunday*